Just For Friends

by Eugénie R. Rocherolle

Eugénie Ricau Rocherolle becomes a friend to many pianists through her piano music. Her warm, creative musical style reflects her personality. She composes mostly by improvising at the piano, beginning with a basic topic or theme, and striving for contrast, humor, catchy rhythms, and good melodies with appealing harmonies.

Mrs. Rocherolle grew up in one of this country's prominent French areas - New Orleans. She spent her college junior year in Paris, where she had a class with Nadia Boulanger. On the return boat from Paris, Eugénie met her future husband. They were married a few years later. In their rural Connecticut home they have raised their daughter and three sons, and are now enjoying grandchildren!

For more piano works by Eugénie Rocherolle, please see the back cover for Solos, Ensembles, Christmas, and Special Circumstances.

ISBN 0-8497-6180-8

© **1990 Neil A. Kjos Music Company**, 4380 Jutland Drive, San Diego, California 92117.
International copyright secured. All rights reserved. Printed in U.S.A.

Intermezzo

to Patricia Johnstone LaCrosse

Eugénie Rocherolle

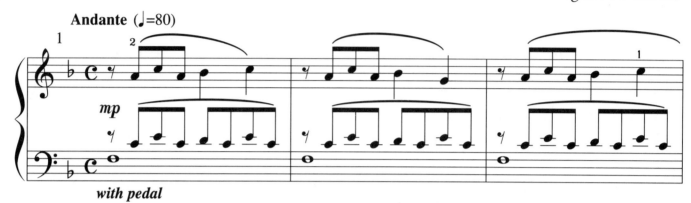

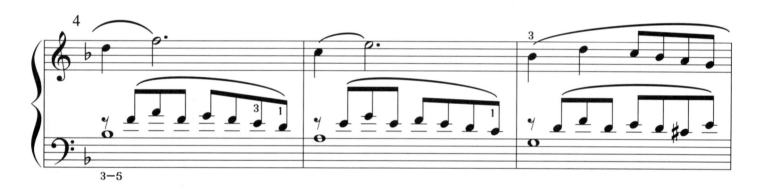

Quiet Nights

to Cecelia Merritt Elvy

Eugénie Rocherolle

An Old-Fashioned Waltz

to Virginia Arnold Ball

Eugénie Rocherolle

Dreamscape

to Carol Giffen Mayfield

Eugénie Rocherolle

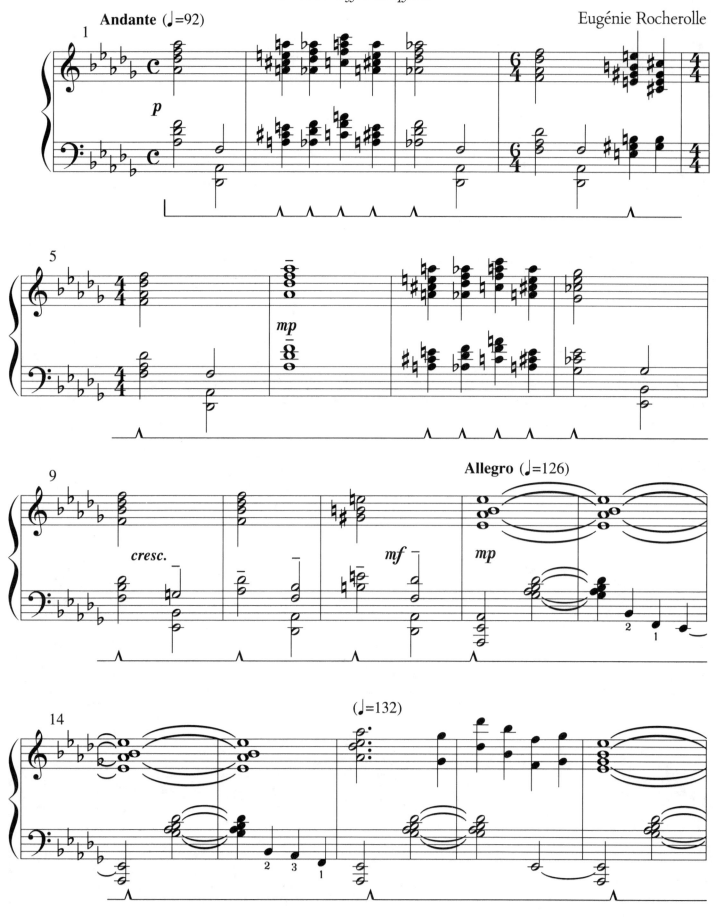

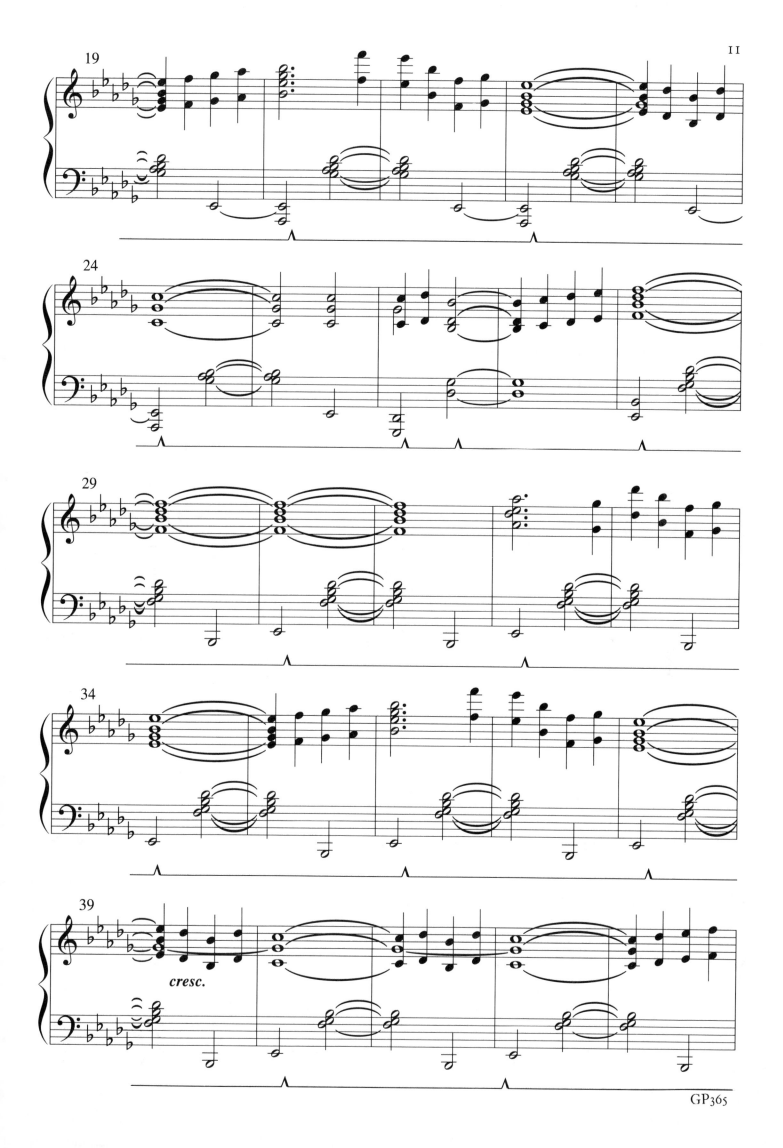

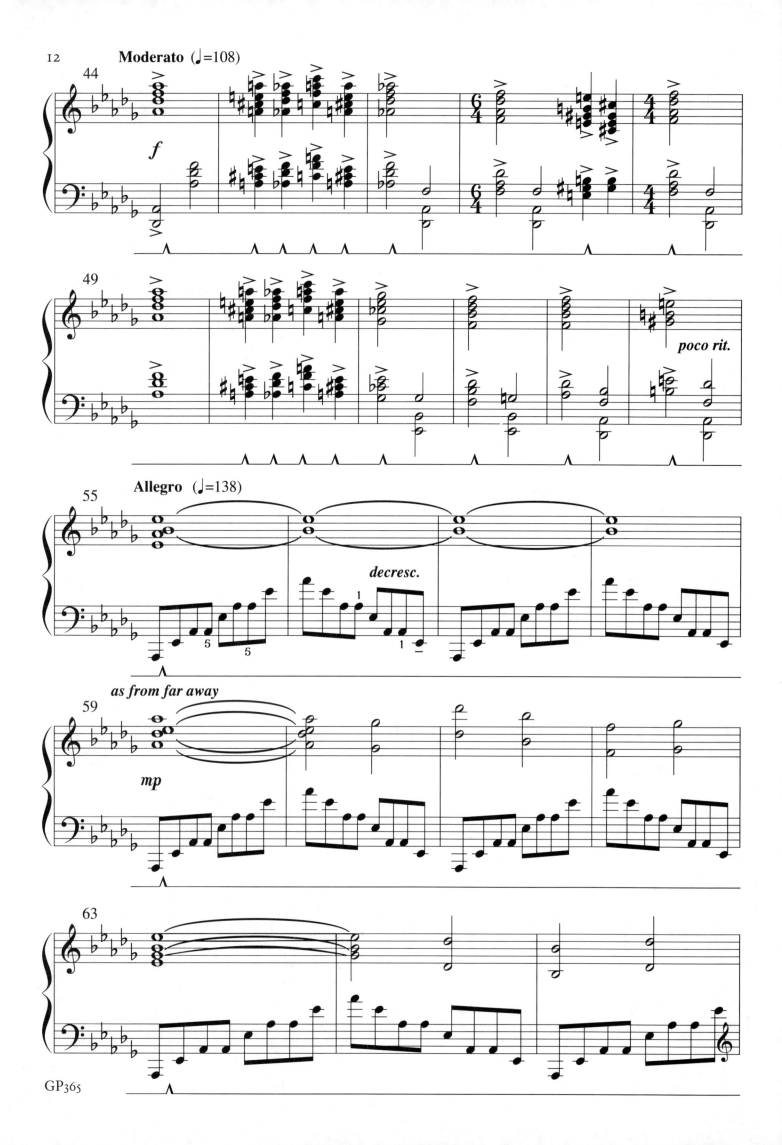

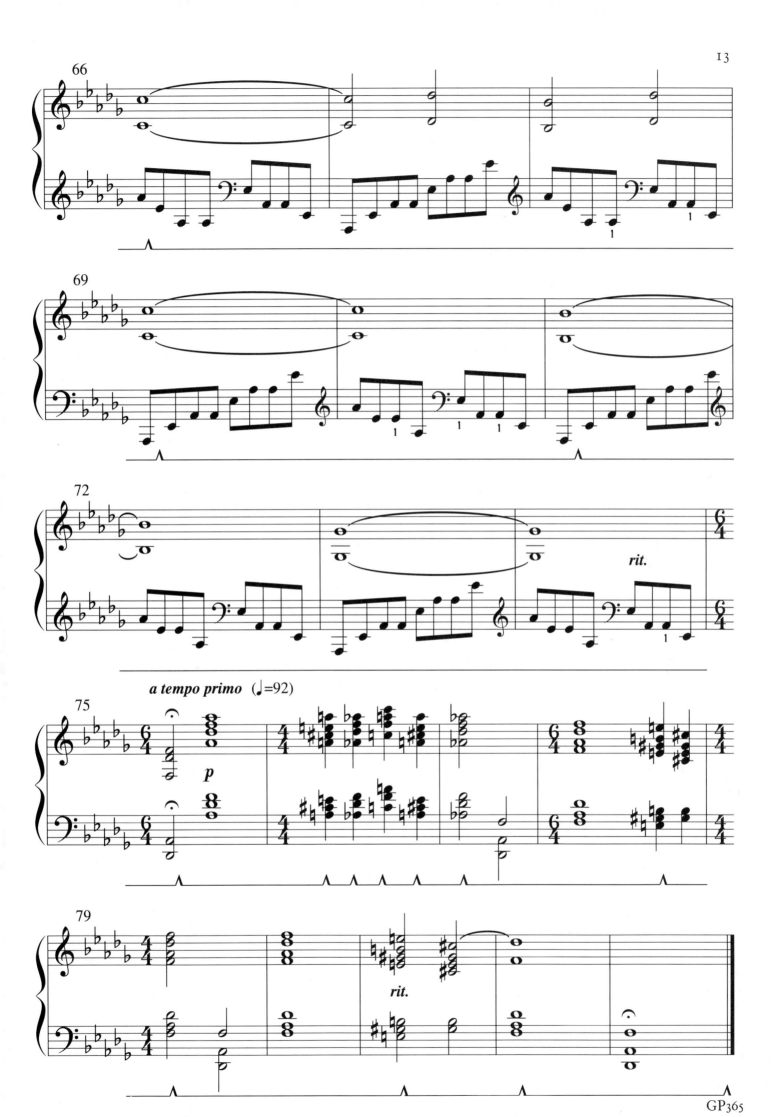

Seaflower

to Louise Galt Pease

Eugénie Rocherolle

Seaflower is the name of a beacon off the coast of Groton Long Point, Connecticut.

Cántico Ibérico

to Carolyn Fynn Lenz

Eugénie Rocherolle

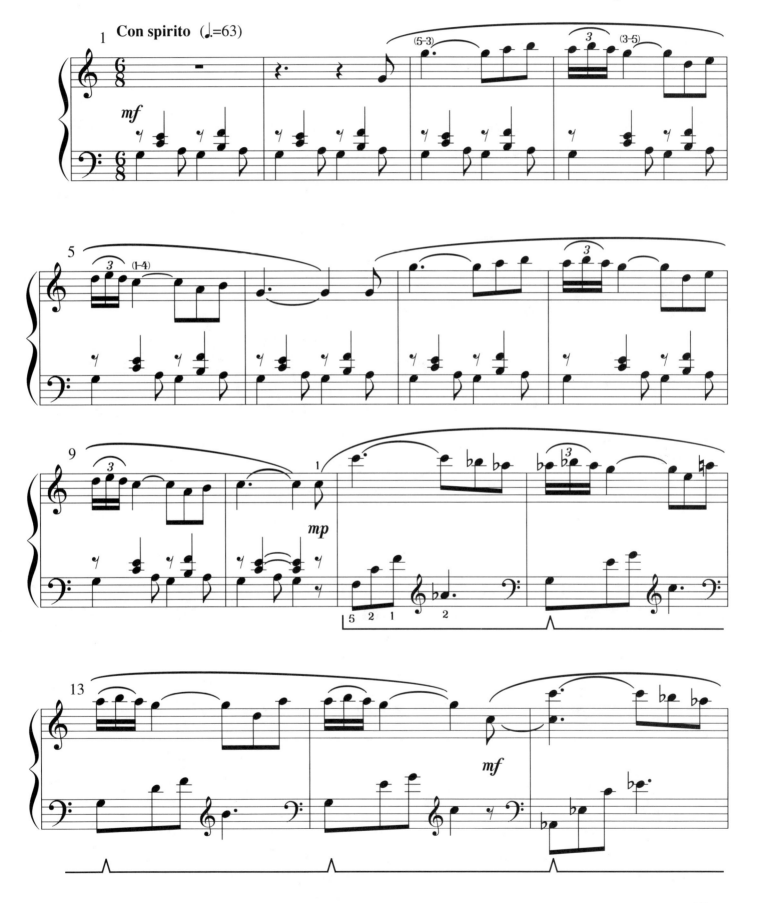

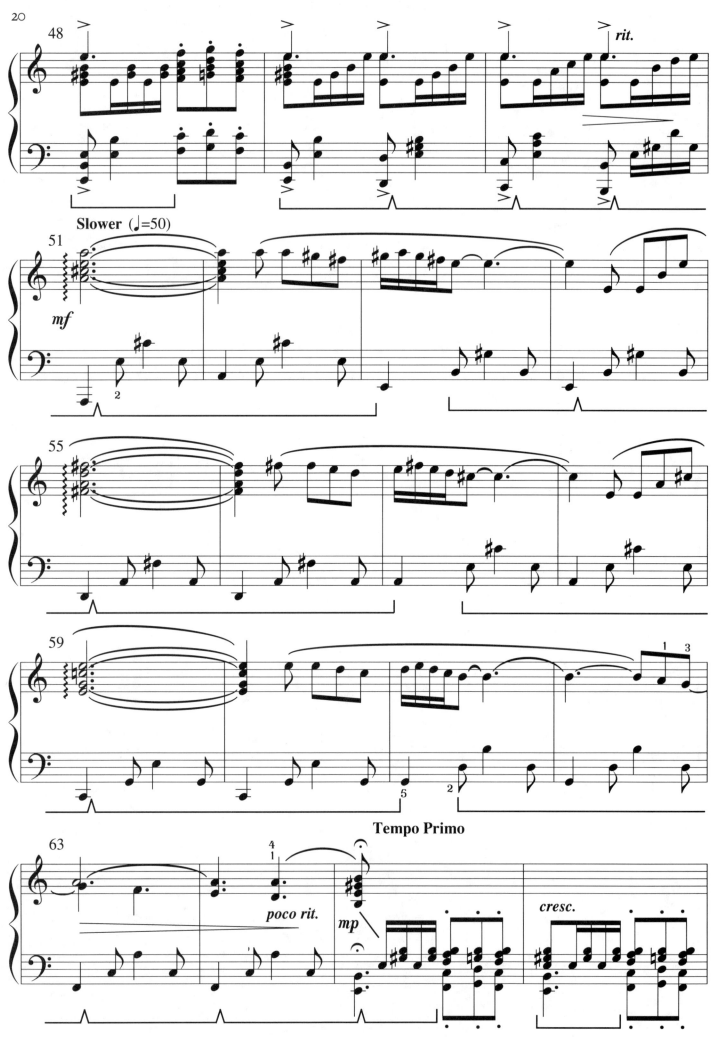